1

Whale man

'Oh, no,' I gasped. 'What's he doing here?'

Dad had come to meet me at the school gates. You'd think I'd be pleased. But I wasn't.

I tried to hide in a crowd of my friends. But Dad spotted me. He waved and shouted, 'Cal!'

I acted as if I hadn't heard.

But then he shouted even louder. 'Cal! Over here! It's me! Dad!'

All my friends stared at him. 'Is that your *dad*?' said Raj, as if he couldn't believe it. He was too polite to say anything else.

But Stevo wasn't. He pushed past me. 'Your dad's a big wobble-man!' he shouted. Some of my friends giggled.

I was cringing inside and my face felt burning hot. I rushed across the road to meet Dad.

'What are you doing here?' I snapped at him.

'That's not a very nice welcome,' Dad said. He looked hurt.

'Come on!' I shouted at Dad. 'Let's get out of here!'

The school buses were revving up in the drive. Soon they'd be driving past us.

Dad started walking.

'Faster, Dad, faster!' I said.

But Dad couldn't go faster. He stumped slowly along. He was already huffing and puffing. 'What's the hurry?' he said.

Oh no! Oh no! I could hear the roar of engines. Those school buses were nearly here.

I could see all those eyes staring from the bus windows. Now, don't get me wrong, I love my dad to bits. I really do. He's good fun. Everyone likes him. But, at that very moment, I was so embarrassed I wished the ground would open and swallow me up.

Then it got worse. Someone yelled from an open window, 'Cal's got a whale for a dad!'

The buses drove off. I looked at Dad. He must have heard. Everyone in the street heard! But Dad didn't say anything. He was busy reading a poster in a shop window.

'Belly dancing!' he cried, suddenly.

'Pardon, Dad?'

'I've been thinking for ages I've got to get fit. I'll go to belly dancing classes.'

'But that's for girls!'

'It says here, "men welcome". You won't believe this, but I used to be a good dancer, once. A real twinkle-toes.'

I should have been horrified. My dad, doing belly dancing! But I wasn't at all worried. Because I was thinking, 'He won't go. He's always saying he's going to get fit – and he never, ever, does.'

9

2

Wibble wobble

I couldn't believe it. Dad *did* go to belly dancing classes.

I told myself, 'He won't like it. He'll never go again.'

But Dad came home really excited after his first class. Mum and I were in the kitchen.

'Want to know how to belly dance?' he asked us.

'I haven't got a belly to dance with,' said Mum, who's quite skinny.

'Doesn't matter!' cried Dad. 'Fat or thin, young or old. Anyone can belly dance!'

Then he did something really embarrassing. I was so glad none of my friends were there to see. He put his arms above his head and started shaking his hips.

'I'm not very good yet,' he said. 'But this is the basic idea.'

His tummy started wibbling, wobbling under his T-shirt. I gazed at it with my mouth hanging open. It was awesome. It was as if it had a life of its own.

'Dad!' I said. 'Dad! Do you have to?'

I was just thinking, 'Can my dad get any more embarrassing?' Then he did.

Dad said, 'The trick is to … sort of … move your tummy in circles. Like this!'

His tummy was rippling in waves, like a stormy sea. It was swinging from side to side.

I said, 'Dad, stop it! You'll hurt yourself. You'll knock the plates off the table!'

I couldn't bear to watch. But Mum seemed impressed. 'That looks like good fun,' she said.

She joined in. This couldn't be happening! Both my parents were belly dancing together round the kitchen. I rushed to close the blinds, in case anyone was peeking in.

'Hey Cal,' said Mum. 'This is great. Why don't you have a go?'

'No way!' I scowled. 'No way! I am never, *ever* going to belly dance!'

3

Nightmare!

One day, Dad rushed home from his belly dancing class.

He said, 'Cal, guess what? My class is giving a belly dancing display at your school.'

I couldn't believe I'd heard him properly. I almost had a heart attack!

'At my school?' I said, in a small voice.

'Yes!' he said. 'It's going to be in assembly, next Friday.'

'In assembly?' I gasped. My legs felt suddenly weak. I had to sit down before I fell down. In assembly? That meant the WHOLE SCHOOL would be there. My friends, Stevo and all the teachers would be there…and Friday was only three days away.

'Dad!' I cried. 'This is terrible! This is a nightmare! You can't do this to me!'

But Dad couldn't see a problem. He was really looking forward to it. He said, 'We want *everyone* to try belly dancing. Even little kids.'

I wanted to say all sorts of things. Like, 'Dad, everyone will laugh at you', and 'Stevo will shout out rude things' and 'I'm going to die of embarrassment'.

But how could I be so cruel? Dad seemed so happy and full of excitement.

'Belly dancing has changed my life,'
Dad said. He turned sideways. 'Look,
don't you think I'm getting trimmer?'

It was true. Dad WAS getting
trimmer. Since he'd started belly
dancing, he'd started eating a healthy
diet with lots of fruit and vegetables.

But, at that moment, I just couldn't
see the good side.

All I was thinking was, 'This Friday is going to be the worst day of my life!'

Why couldn't he get fit by jogging or going to the gym, like other dads? Why, oh why, did he have to choose belly dancing?

'Maybe this display on Friday won't happen,' I tried to comfort myself. 'Maybe Dad will get a cold. Maybe the school will fall down.'

But Wednesday passed and Thursday.

Nothing happened.

Dad hadn't even got a sniffle and my school was still standing.

By Friday morning I was panicking.

I tried to get out of going to school. Well, wouldn't you? I came down to breakfast looking pale.

I said, 'Mum, I feel really ill. I can't go to school today.'

'Of course you can,' Mum said in a bright and chirpy voice.

She handed me my packed lunch. 'Besides, you don't want to miss your dad's belly dancing display, do you? He'd be upset if you weren't there to see him.'

'But Mum!'

She pushed me out of the door.

I trudged along the road, muttering to myself. I was hoping that my school might have fallen down in the night. But I turned the corner and it was still there.

With a face like doom, I dragged myself through the school gates.

4

The big surprise

The school hall had filled right up, with rows and rows of little kids and big kids. Our teachers were sitting on chairs down the sides.

Mrs Phillips, our head teacher, was up on the stage. She's quite scary and strict. She doesn't smile very often.

I was thinking, 'Maybe the fire alarm will ring. Maybe there'll be a fire drill.'

Then Mrs Phillips started saying, 'Now, children, we have a big surprise for you,' and I knew that nothing was going to save me.

'The belly dancing class from the Sports Centre,' said Mrs Phillips, 'has kindly agreed to put on a display.' Mrs Phillips gave us her hard stare. 'I expect you children to sit still and be quiet.'

I was already squirming with embarrassment. Then Dad came on stage.

He was the only man in a crowd of women! I could feel my cheeks turning fiery red.

Maybe no one would recognise Dad?

But, of course, Stevo did. He started grinning and then he shouted out loud, 'Hey, that's Cal's dad!'

People turned and stared at me.

I wished I could shrivel up, as small as a slug. Then I could slither away under a stone.

I was thinking, 'Please, Dad, don't!'

Then some music began blasting out. Dad started dancing, with his tummy going round like a washing machine on spin.

All the dancers were moving to the
music. They'd got big smiles on their
faces. They were shaking clappers and
little tinkling bells and some were even
banging drums. They looked as if they
were having a really good time.

A little kid started rocking to the beat.
But then she remembered she was
supposed to sit still and stopped.

Suddenly Dad shouted from the stage in a big voice, 'Come on, kids! Come on, teachers! Get up here and join us!'

No one moved. No one dared. Mrs Phillips had told us to sit still.

I was wriggling in my seat and thinking, 'Shut up, Dad, shut UP!'

Then, all of a sudden, Dad danced towards Mrs Phillips.

I couldn't believe it! Had my dad
gone completely out of his mind?
He was trying to get our head
teacher to belly dance! She looked
stern and shook her head.

But Dad didn't give up.

He roared out, 'Come on, Mrs
Phillips, have a go. *Everyone* can belly
dance!'

He took her hand and led her into
the middle of the dancers.

The whole school stared in amazement. Everyone's mouth was hanging open. Mrs Phillips started jigging about. She was even smiling. I think she was enjoying herself!

Then Dad yelled out again, 'Come and join us, kids! Your head teacher says it's OK.'

Some little children rushed on stage. They're always the first. You could see they wanted to have a go. My dad handed out musical instruments. More kids were going onto the stage, or standing up and dancing in the hall.

Suddenly, our whole school was dancing and clapping to the music. Kids, teachers, everyone.

Then, suddenly, I realised I was swaying too. I just couldn't help it. The music was catching, like chicken pox. The frown on my face was going away. Instead, I couldn't stop grinning.

One of my friends danced by. 'Hey Cal!' she called out. 'Your dad is a star!'

I shouted back, above the music and bells and drums. 'You don't have to tell me. I know!'

About the author

I was at the swimming pool. I saw a notice: BELLY DANCING CLASSES. The classes weren't in the pool, of course (I don't think you *can* belly dance and swim at the same time!) but in a church hall. The notice also said: *Men and Women Welcome.*

I wondered what my children would say if their dad started belly dancing – and that's how I thought of this story.